Welcome

Synergy Creative Community are a mental health user led and user run community organisation. Synergy take a creative approach to mental wellbeing, running weekly sessions of art, improvised music, poetry, cooking for wellbeing, mindfulness meditation and a space to connect with others and share experiences. Synergy Food Project began in 2011 exploring the links between what we eat and how we feel. Each week lunch is created by a team of volunteers guided by Abi, Nutritional Therapist at Nutrition For Change. The group then come together as a family to enjoy a delicious and nutritious meal.

Odi Oquosa – Manager. Liz Ikamba – Project Co-ordinator

Spicy Falafel and Watercress
Hummus   7
Walnut and Corn Bread,
Rocket and Walnut Pesto   9
Red lentil and coconut dhal   11
Beans and Greens   13
Sally's Greek Salad and
Potato Salad   15
Simon's Veg Stew   16
Traditional Chickpea Curry   17
Chickpea Pancakes with
Toasted Cumin Seeds   18
Seasonal Frittata   19
Community Salad   21

"Follow our bodies rather than what is in our minds" says Tam "The communal nature of eating is important to Synergy members. It is this family sense of recovery that enables members to find happier and hopefully healthier eating habits. This, of course, is an individual thing for each person who is affected by mental illness. Our individual values are often rooted in the traditions we grew up around. Cooking and eating together with Synergy encourages people to gain insight, and become more mindful about what we eat"
Tamsin, Synergy Member

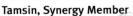

Introduction

Good food choices, along with social support and adequate sleep are really the foundation stones for managing all that comes our way in life. Statistics like "1 in 4 people will experience some kind of mental health problem in the course of a year" are a stark reminder of the prevalence of mental health problems in our society. Although food and nutrition is no panacea, it's a frequently missed area that everyone can have some level of choice and control over. From both my personal and clinical experience the key areas that are important to focus on in building these foundations are:

1) Eating foods as close to how they occur in nature as possible

Michael Pollan's Eater's Manifesto in his book *In Defence Of Food* simply states: "Eat food. Not too much. Mostly plants". These are robust guidelines with which to live by, ensuring variety in the diet and avoidance of empty calories from processed foods.

2) Ensuring adequate essential fats in the diet

Given that the brain is made up mostly of fat it is not surprising that a plentiful supply is essential. A balanced ratio of omega-3 and omega-6 fatty acids is necessary for a healthy brain. A diet rich in oily fish, seeds and nuts whilst avoiding trans fats in processed foods will help keep the brain well nourished.

3) Sufficient levels of vitamins and minerals from a variety of fruits and vegetables

Blanchflower *et al* (2012) found that mental wellbeing and happiness were highest amongst those who ate seven portions of fruit and vegetables a day.

4) Adequate rest and relaxation

Sleep is vital for the body to rebuild and renew. Around 8 hours is recommended for adults to ensure optimum functioning. Sleep can be affected by a diet high in sugar and stimulants and eating too late at night. Leave at least 2 hours after eating and avoid caffeinated drinks after midday. Eating plenty of magnesium rich dark green vegetables as part of your evening meal can help aid relaxation and sleep.

5) Social support - connection to people and nature

Social interaction and contact with nature are fundamental to our sense of being connected to the world. Volunteering on a food growing or gardening project is one way of making and sustaining that connection with nature, food and other people.

Abi Denyer-Bewick
Nutrition For Change

Synergy Rainbow Salsa

Serves 6

"Eat a rainbow everyday". This dish will help to remind you just how tasty that can be. The wider the variety of colour in our diets, the wider the range of nutrients. These mexican flavours would complement a mexican bean stew or be great at a barbecue with meat or fish. Try mashing a ripe avocado and use as a dip alongside the salsa.

Ingredients

- 225g cherry tomatoes – halved
- 1 red onion – finely chopped
- 1 small tin of sweetcorn
- large handful of fresh coriander
- 1 green pepper
- zest and juice of ½ lime
- 1 red or green chilli – deseeded and finely chopped
- olive oil to dress

Method

Mix all ingredients together and dress with oil and lime juice prior to serving

"Cooking and eating at Synergy helped remind me that I really like healthy food and feel better if I spend a bit of time making myself something with fresh ingredients"
Synergy Member

Out To Lunch With Synergy

"The most peaceful communities are those that embrace human diversity and that are connected by food grown, cooked and shared with love"

Michele Margolis Editor of the Permaculture Diary and Calendar

"I had lots of fun making cutlery and the candelabra. I'm glad people liked what I made"

Jasmine – Synergy Member

"It's so much nicer to eat with other people, I forgot because I have eaten alone for so long"

Synergy Member

Top tip no.1

Cook in bulk. Cooking in batches means that you've got something for a rainy day. Cooking one pot dishes and splitting them into portions gives you lunch for the next day. If you have a freezer, dishes can be frozen and defrosted when you don't have time to cook from scratch.

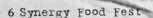

Synergy Spicy Falafels

These falafels are tasty hot or cold so make a great picnic or packed lunch food. Chickpeas are an excellent source of fibre, Vitamin B6 and Iron.

Ingredients

- 3 tbsp coconut oil or sunflower oil
- 2 small onions
- 3 garlic cloves
- small handful parsley – finely chopped
- small handful coriander – finely chopped
- 1 red chilli chopped finely
- 2 tsp cumin
- 2 tsp paprika
- ½ to 1 egg beaten – add gradually, probably won't need it all
- 1 tin chickpeas – rinsed and drained
- ½ cup gram flour plus more to coat before frying

Method

1 Fry onion and garlic over a low heat for 5 minutes until soft

2 Tip into a bowl with chickpeas and dried spices

3 Use hand blender to blend until only a few chunks remain, stir in fresh herbs, egg and gram flour

4 Roll mixture into balls and squash flat into patties. Coat both sides of the falafel in gram flour

5 Heat remaining oil and fry patties for 3 minutes on each side

Serve hot with a salad and homemade hummus

Watercress Hummus

Hummus is a good source of vegetarian protein due to the tahini and chickpeas. A great way to eat raw garlic too – especially helpful if you feel you are coming down with a cold or sore throat.

Ingredients

- 1 x 410g tin of chickpeas rinsed and drained
- 1 tbsp lemon juice
- 1 bag organic watercress
- 2 cloves garlic, crushed
- 1 tsp ground cumin
- 1 tbsp tahini
- 1 tbsp fresh flat leaf parsley leaves, chopped
- 1 tbsp extra virgin olive oil
- freshly ground black pepper

Method

Blend all the ingredients in a food processor or with a hand blender. More garlic, spices, lemon or oil can be added as you blend depending on taste and desired consistency.

Do 1 Thing Different Today...

Here are some ideas and suggestions from Synergy members
I feel better...

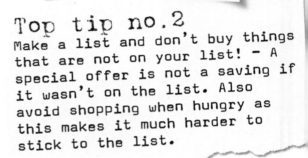

"When I drink more water and less coffee"

"When I add nuts and seeds to my breakfasts and salads"

"If I eat at least 2 green vegetables everyday"

"When I eat at regular intervals throughout the day"

"If my meals are colourful and cheery"

Top tip no. 2

Make a list and don't buy things that are not on your list! — A special offer is not a saving if it wasn't on the list. Also avoid shopping when hungry as this makes it much harder to stick to the list.

"If I treat myself to fresh ingredients"

"If I eat less sugar — swapping biscuits for fruit and nuts is great"

"If I plan ahead what I'm going to eat that day"

"If I eat with other people"

"When I eat breakfast every morning"

"If I see mealtimes as an opportunity to take care of myself"

Walnut and Corn Bread

A great gluten free high protein bread alternative, any nuts or seeds could be ground and used. This is delicious with stews, soups or ratatouille and also works well with hummus in picnics or in a packed lunch box.

Ingredients

- 150g walnuts ground into a fine flour (use a food processor or the grinder attachment with the hand blender)
- 150g cornmeal or polenta
- 4 tsp baking powder
- 225ml milk (dairy or rice)
- 3 eggs
- 5 tbsp groundnut oil or coconut oil

Method

1 Place all dry ingredients in large bowl and mix together
2 Mix wet ingredients (eggs and oil) in a jug
3 Pour wet ingredients into dry ingredients until you have a runny dough
4 Pour into a lined baking tin (for a chunky bread use a 20cm x 30cm 3cm deep baking tray)
5 Cook at 180°C/Gas Mark 4/350°F for 25 minutes

"I made the pesto at home and my daughter loves it, a great way to get more greens into her diet"

Tamsin – Synergy Member

Rocket and Walnut Pesto

Rocket is a great source of vitamin A and vitamin C whilst walnuts provide omega 3 fatty acids, protein and magnesium. These are all essential brain nutrients.

Ingredients

- 2 handfuls rocket
- 2 cloves of garlic
- zest and juice of one lemon
- 2 handfuls of walnuts
- small handful of fresh parsley
- olive oil

Method

Another recipe for the hand blender and grinder attachment – the most useful kitchen implement.
1 Grind the walnuts in the grinder attachment until finely ground
2 Add all ingredients to a large bowl and gently mix with the hand blender adding oil gradually to the mixture to get the consistency that you desire
- Great stirred through rice, quinoa or new potatoes
- This could also be made with seeds – delicious with pumpkin seeds or sunflower seeds and in the winter is delicious with kale instead of rocket

Why is it good to eat seasonally?

The joys of eating seasonally cannot be underestimated. It can mean both better taste and better value – whilst also having a positive effect on the environment. There is also the pleasure of looking forward to a certain food season and making the most of it – for example enjoying the sweetness of English strawberries in June/July or the brief few weeks of Spring when the asparagus are ready.

Seasonal eating helps us to stay in touch with nature and our ancestors whilst helping us to save money.

There are also health benefits dating back to hunter-gatherer times when we depended on nature to provide us with the nutrients essential to get us through the following seasons. An example of this would be stocking up with leafy green vegetables as the weather gets colder so that our immune systems benefit from plenty of vitamin C as well as Magnesium and Zinc to get us through the winter.

Top tip no.3

Buy ingredients rather than ready made dishes. Fresh ingredients, especially when in season are likely to be cheaper than ready made, processed foods such as jars of sauces or ready meals. These are also likely to contain added sugar, salt or preservatives. The more food that you cook from scratch the more money you will save.

Red Lentil and Coconut Dhal

The spices in this dish are not only delicious and colourful but offer health benefits too. Turmeric, garlic and ginger all contain compounds found to have anti-inflammatory properties. For variation any other vegetables can be added to the curry. Green beans, aubergine and fresh tomatoes would be delicious in summer. Try adding butternut squash or parsnips in winter.

Ingredients

- 250g red lentils
- 8 small onions
- 1 bulb garlic
- thumb length of ginger
- 2 chilli red bird eye (with seeds)
- 2 tbsp toasted mustard seeds
- 2 tsp ground coriander
- 2 tsp ground cumin
- 1 tbsp garam masala
- 1 tablespoon ground turmeric
- tin of tomatoes
- 600ml (ish) vegetable stock
- juice of 1 lime
- fresh coriander
- pinch of ground cloves
- ground cardamom seeds
- 2 handfuls desiccated coconut

Method

1 Toast the mustard seeds in a dry pan for a couple of minutes, moving them around constantly to avoid burning and remove from the pan

2 Blend the onion, garlic, ginger, chilli and mustard seeds into a thick paste with a hand blender. Add a little water

3 Fry the onion paste and stir in the dry red lentils, once covered add in the dried spices (except the garam masala) to coat the lentils

4 Add the tinned tomatoes and vegetable stock and bring to the boil. Cover and simmer, stirring occasionally and adding any extra liquid if necessary. Add coconut and stir in

5 Once the lentils are cooked and soft, add the lime juice, garam masala and chopped coriander. Serve with brown basmati rice or chick pea pancakes

Shopping experiences

We explored some of the issues that can impact on the food choices that we make and came up with some creative solutions. In discussing some of these factors we found that many people had very similar experiences, but had thought they were the only one. Synergy provides a supportive environment for sharing experiences with people reporting that they feel less isolated as a result.

"Volunteering in the kitchen reminded me that I do like to create food, especially for other people and that using fresh ingredients means that delicious dishes are often a combination of only a few ingredients"
Synergy Member

Shopping with others was more enjoyable

Grow my own

Order shopping online

Go to smaller shops / farms

Where can I find my food?

Set up food swap club with friends

Join a box delivery scheme

Local community gardens

Eat at parents

EXPLORE SOME OTHER OPTIONS

Top tip no.4
Share your food. Food bought in bulk can often work out cheaper. Get together with a friend and split large fresh items such as cabbages or bags of carrots. Purchase wholegrains and other organic foods from a local group. In Brighton try the Brighton Unemployed Centre www.bucfp.org/food-project/allganics

Beans and Greens

This is a great dish for adapting to the seasons, during spring use leeks and spinach, in summer spring onions and chard, in autumn kale and onions and in winter onions and cabbage. The beans are a nutritious source of protein and the greens provide valuable B vitamins, important for making energy and minerals such as zinc and magnesium.

Ingredients

- 3 leeks – finely chopped into circles
- 2 cloves of garlic – crushed
- 2 tins of butter beans – drained and rinsed
- 1 tin of kidney beans – drained and rinsed
- handful parsley, finely chopped
- 1 bag curly kale – shredded roughly

Method

1 Cook the leeks and garlic together in oil until soft
2 Add the finely chopped parsley
3 Add the rinsed beans and stir until coated with the garlic and parsley
4 Add chopped kale or spring greens until lightly wilted

Serve alone or as accompaniment to grilled fish Any leftovers can be whizzed up into a delicious soup eaten with chunky bread.

Quick, tasty, healthy by Duncan

Frozen peas steamed with butter, melted through with a pinch of salt (5 mins) and cayenne pepper on a bed of fish fingers (15 mins) with Uncle Bens rice (10 mins)

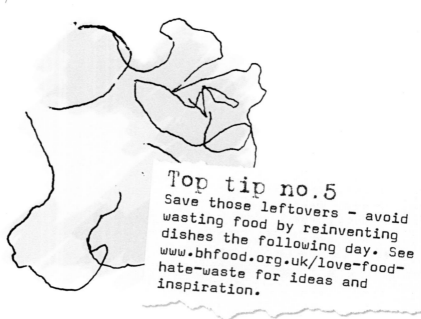

"So for the first time in my life 3 weeks ago I made some gravy with my fish fingers and peas. Although gravy is not something associated with fish fingers and peas I needed some kind of sauce to go with this just to make it more interesting. In some way I wanted to make a dish vaguely remembering mum's home cooking. The smell is nice and comforting and the taste is very nice and meaty and salty. For the first time I was cooking for myself out of love."

Top tip no.5

Save those leftovers - avoid wasting food by reinventing dishes the following day. See www.bhfood.org.uk/love-food-hate-waste for ideas and inspiration.

Sally's Greek Salad

Sally's version of a traditional greek salad contains a wider range of colours and plenty of fibre. Beetroot is a great source of iron, avocado is rich in vitamin E, whilst also helping us to absorb nutrients from other vegetables. Olives are very nutritious – rich in vitamin A, vitamin E, iron and zinc.

Serves **6**

Ingredients

- 2 beef tomatoes – thinly sliced
- 50g black olives – halved
- 50g green olives stuffed with chilli
- 2 small red onions – finely chopped
- 1 cucumber – cubed
- cooked beetroot – cubed
- 1 avocado – sliced to scatter on top
- 1 packet Greek feta cheese

Method

1 Chop and mix together
2 Add sea salt and ground red/green/black pepper to taste

Delicious served with grilled fish or as part of a picnic with a potato salad.

Potato Salad

New potatoes are a slower releasing carbohydrate than older potatoes as well as being high in vitamin C and potassium.

Serves **6**

Ingredients

- 10 medium sized new potatoes
- handful fresh oregano, mint or thyme
- 1 chopped red onion or bunch of spring onions
- 1 tbsp mayonnaise
- pinch of sea salt

Method

1 Boil 10 medium sized new potatoes for around 20 minutes until tender
2 Drain and place in a large bowl
3 Add onions, mayonnaise and fresh herbs
4 Season with salt and pepper

"Synergy lunch is so full of colour and vibrancy, when I feel well I try to include as many colours as I can at home"
Synergy Member

Simon's Vegetable Stew

This is a nourishing meal to have on a winter's day. A great way to use up whatever is in the fridge. The wider the range of vegetables the wider the range of nutrients. Broccoli and cauliflower are rich in soluble fibre and sulphurous compounds called glucosinolates which are protective for the body. Parsley is a good source of folic acid and iron.

Serves 4

Ingredients

- 1 large onion
- 4 carrots
- head of broccoli
- small cauliflower
- 6 medium size potatoes
- 250g mushrooms
- 3 stalks of celery
- can of kidney beans
- tin of tomato purée
- vegetable stock

Optional: Chilli for a kick. Add cornflour if you want to make the sauce thicker. You could also add herbs like oregano and parsley.

Also instead of potatoes you could have rice and/or crusty bread.

Method

1 Finely chop the onion
2 Chop all the vegetables – most of these are nice left quite chunky
3 Open the can of kidney beans and tomato purée
4 Fry the onion
5 Add the mushrooms
6 Add all the remaining vegetables
7 Add the vegetable stock and tomato purée
8 Cook for around 15-20 minutes. Make sure vegetables are tender
9 Add kidney beans
10 Enjoy!

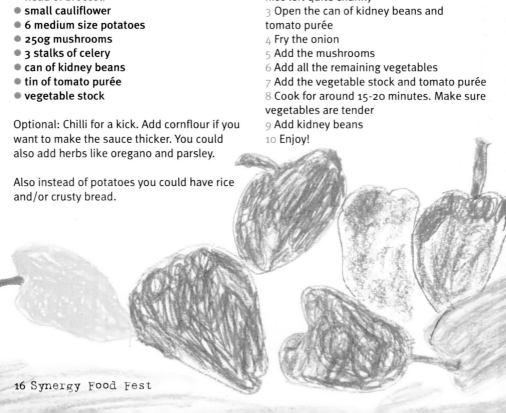

Chickpeas Curry with Rice

1. Fry Onions with Olive oil
2. Add 2 tomato tins
3. Add Salt + Spices + Mix together for 3 minutes
4. Add 4 x Chickpeas tins
5. Stir and cook for ã 20/25 Mins.

Top tip no.6

Plan Ahead - a bit of time spent planning, for the next few days or just the following day, can help to encourage healthier choices, save money and prevent waste.

Chickpea Pancakes with Toasted Cumin Seeds

A healthier lower fat alternative to naan bread.

Makes **6**

Ingredients

- 2 handfuls cumin seeds
- 150g chickpea flour (gram flour)
- 1 egg
- 200ml water

Method

1 Sieve flour and then add the egg

2 Stir in enough water to make the batter smooth – if you have a hand blender this will make the batter even smoother

3 Dry roast the cumin seeds in a pan before adding them to the mixture

4 Using a ladle add the batter to a well oiled frying pan and cook until the edges are golden, turn over with a spatula

5 Cook for another minute on the other side

6 Remove from the pan and keep warm whilst making the other pancakes

Top tip no.7

Choose cheaper cuts of meat – buying chicken thighs or wings rather than breast. Organ meats such as liver and kidneys make a good alternative to steak. It may be possible to buy better quality meat if trying the cheaper cuts.

Vegetable Frittata

Serves 2

A frittata is a great way to use up whatever veg you have left and the egg provides a wholesome vegetarian protein. This can be eaten both hot and cold making it an ideal dinner one night and lunch the next day.

Ingredients

- 4 eggs
- 1 small tin sweetcorn
- large handful frozen petit pois peas
- 2 small leeks chopped finely
- 12 cherry tomatoes
- mixed herbs – mint, parsley and basil work well
- 1 tbsp olive oil or coconut oil

Method

1 Preheat the oven to 200°C (180°C fan or Gas Mark 6)
2 Saute the leeks and tomatoes (or whatever seasonal veg you are using) in a pan with ½ tablespoon of oil, add the chopped herbs
3 Cook until the leeks soften
4 Add the peas and sweetcorn and stir to mix. Pour mixture into an oven proof dish
5 Beat the eggs and pour over the vegetables
6 Bake in a hot oven for 30 minutes until the top is beginning to colour

This one was made at the height of the asparagus season and was particularly tasty!

Bowl of root veg pared to perfection,
Water bubbles, awaiting sand of grain,
Aroma of curry wafts through West Hill Hall
It's Synergy Lunch Preparation Time again!
Sarah – Synergy Member

The process of creating the beautiful artwork involved exploring food with all of our senses reminding us that food and eating are so much more than just something we have to do each day...

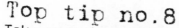

Top tip no.8
Take your time to eat - digestion does not work effectively if meals are rushed or eaten on the move. Sit down and savour every mouthful and eating can become a meditation practice, nourishing body, mind and spirit.

"[creating food art] encourages me to think about food and eating, whereas I will otherwise go without eating or be unable to eat"
Toni – Synergy Member

"It's a really fun way to think about food. Now I think cooking might be fun too"
Synergy Member

"I love food and always thought of cooking as a creative adventure but never imagined I could draw anything. It meant so much to me to have my drawings validated by others in the group"
Synergy Member

"Drawing with the cauliflower behind my back helped me to focus on the bumps and curves, I also thought a lot about it's unusual texture. It was fun to use different senses to experience food"
Synergy Member

Synergy Community Salad

Summer Dressing

Ingredients picked and eaten immediately are packed with nutrients, and nothing beats the whole experience of discovering, picking and eating wild foods. When foraging for wild plants take care to identify things before you munch.

Ingredients

- 2 tablespoons olive oil
- 4 chopped mint leaves
- 2 teaspoons tahini
- splash of cider vinegar

Ingredients

Things that are growing in a park or garden near you!!

This salad was created from a mixture of **rainbow chard, spinach, rocket, red orach, oak leaf lettuce, violets, pansies, chives, celery and borage flowers.** These were all found in Dyke Road Park Community Garden in Brighton.

Method

Mix together in a jar, replace the lid and shake vigorously before dressing the leafy foraged salad

Method

Chop and mix ingredients together and add edible flowers on the top

The Prime Minister danced with
the grapefruit. The banana was a bit too
suggestive. Round and smooth like a
woman's breast. Yellow and joyous he
smoothed it in his arms. The Prime
Minister's wife chose a tomato; rich, red and
promiscuous. The tomato was fruity despite
being classed with the vegetables. She was
challenging stereotypes. Meanwhile she was
being eclipsed by the grapefruit. She
stabbed out and severed the grapefruit
from her husband's hands. From now on no
more trips to the fruit-seller's stands.
Last time it had been a melon. The stress
of ruling the country was taking its toll.
The Prime Minister loved to dance but could
not do the difficult moves, so fruit let him
off the hook somewhat. He'd tried salsa
and meringue but all that twirling just
made the vegetables seasick.
Sally – Synergy Member